Angela Llanas
Libby Williams

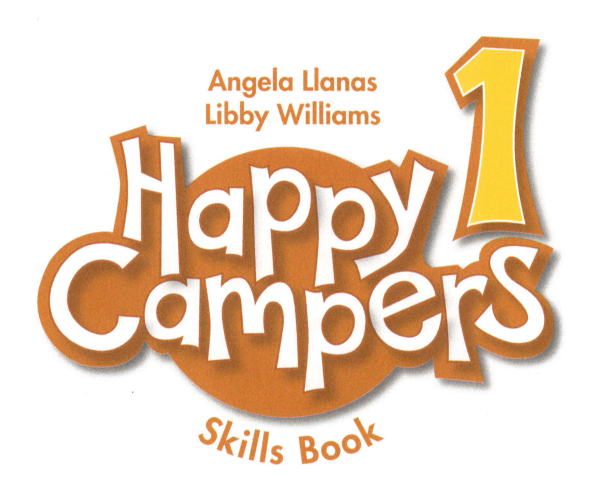

Happy Campers 1

Skills Book

Skills Scope and Sequence

Unit	Page	Picture Talk	Happy Reader
1	4	**Speaking and Listening Skills:** Point to parts of a picture and talk about them.	**Reading Skill:** Identify characters.
2	10	**Speaking and Listening Skills:** Ask and answer questions about a picture.	**Reading Skill:** Recall details.
3	16	**Speaking and Listening Skills:** Ask and answer questions about a picture.	**Reading Skill:** Identify characters.
4	22	**Speaking and Listening Skills:** Point to parts of a picture and talk about them.	**Reading Skill:** Recall details.
5	28	**Speaking and Listening Skills:** Ask and answer questions about a picture.	**Reading Skill:** Draw conclusions.
6	34	**Speaking and Listening Skills:** Point to parts of a picture and talk about them.	**Reading Skill:** Recall details.
7	40	**Speaking and Listening Skills:** Make statements about a picture and respond.	**Reading Skill:** Draw conclusions.
8	46	**Speaking and Listening Skills:** Point to parts of a picture and talk about them.	**Reading Skill:** Recall details.

Happy Writer	Word Work
Writing Skill: Identify and understand characters. Happy Writer **Page 52**	**Consonant Sound:** m **Vowel Sound:** short a mad
Writing Skill: Recall details. Happy Writer **Page 52**	**Consonant Sound:** h **Vowel Sound:** short o hop
Writing Skill: Identify and understand characters. Happy Writer **Page 53**	**Consonant Sound:** r **Vowel Sound:** short u run
Writing Skill: Sequence events. Happy Writer **Page 53**	**Consonant Sound:** f **Vowel Sound:** long i five
Writing Skill: Identify and understand setting. Happy Writer **Page 54**	**Consonant Sound:** p **Vowel Sound:** short e pen
Writing Skill: Identify and understand setting. Happy Writer **Page 54**	**Consonant Sound:** b **Vowel Sound:** long e bee
Writing Skill: Identify and understand characters. Happy Writer **Page 55**	**Consonant Sound:** w **Vowel Sound:** long a wave
Writing Skill: Personalize the story. Happy Writer **Page 55**	**Consonant Sound:** th **Vowel Sound:** short i think

UNIT 1 Picture Talk

1 Look at the picture. Find and complete.

1. B _y_ _e_ !

2. G_____!

3. H_____!

4. H__!

2 Point and say.

Happy Reader

1 52 Read and listen.

Family Fun

1 Hi! Hello!

2 My name's Jo. What's your name?

This is my dad and my brother, Brad.

This is my mom and my sister, Kim.

3 This is my happy family. My mom, my dad, my brother, my sister, and me!

4 We aren't mad! We are glad!

Hot dogs for lunch. Munch, munch!

5 Bye!

2 Point and say the names of Jo's family.

Happy Writer **Page 52**

Word Work

1 🐶 53 **Listen and chant.**

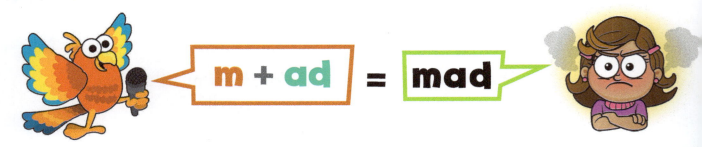

2 **Say and circle the words with the *m* sound.**

1. munch

2. mom

3. dad

3 Look and say. Then complete.

1. m ___ d   2. d ___ d   3. h ___ p p y

4  Say it!

> My mom and dad are happy!

UNIT 2 — Picture Talk

1 Look at the picture. Find and complete.

1.
I'm s__ v__.

2.
I'm o__e.

3.
I'm __ gh__.

4.
I'm __i__.

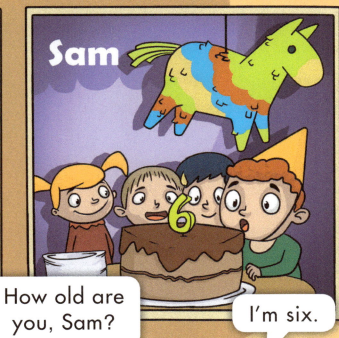

How old are you, Sam?

I'm six.

2) Ask and answer.

Happy Reader

1   **Read and listen.**

Hopscotch Winner

1

Helen: Hi, Harry! I'm Helen! How old are you?

Harry: I'm seven years old.

Helen: Hey! Me too!

Helen: I have an eraser. Let's play hopscotch!

Harry: And I have some crayons. Get ready to hop!

2

Harry: Hop, Helen, hop!

Helen: Box number one! Now two, three, four, five, six, seven, eight, nine, ten! And back again!

Harry: Stop, Helen, stop!

Helen: Ten, nine, eight, seven, six, five, four, three, two, one! This is fun!

3

Helen: Hop, Harry, hop!

Harry: One! Two, three, four, five, six, seven, eight! Oh, no!

Helen: Oh, Harry!

4

Harry: Hooray, Helen! Hopscotch winner!

2 Circle the hopscotch winner.

Word Work

1 🐶 56 **Listen and chant.**

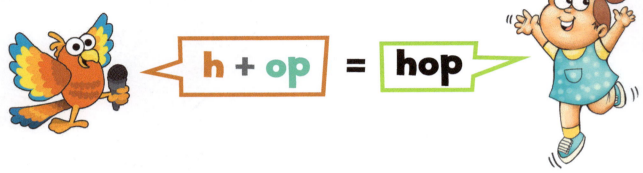

h + op = hop

2 Say and circle the words with the *h* sound.

1. (happy)

2. pencil

3. hi

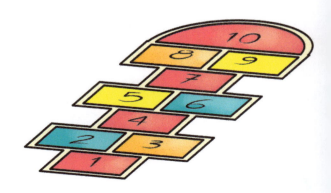

4. hopscotch

3 Say, write, and match.

hop

4 Say it!

Hi, Mom! Stop and play hopscotch!

UNIT 3   Picture Talk

1 Look at the picture. Find and check (✓) or cross (✗).

1.
   cat

2.
   rabbit

3.
   opossum

4.
   horse

5.
   alligator

6.
   dog

Happy Reader

1 58 **Read and listen.**

Kitty Cat

1
What's that?
It isn't an owl.

No! It's my kitty cat!

Run, Mrs. Kent.
Run, run, run.

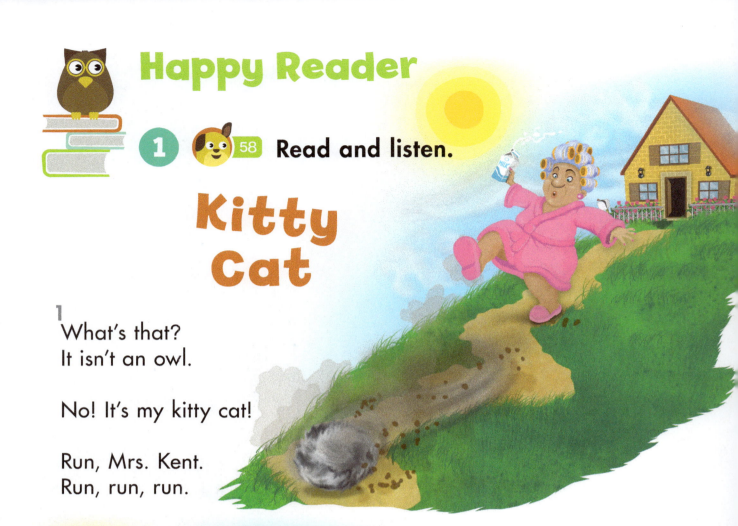

2
What's that?
It isn't a bear.

No! It's my kitty cat!

Run, Farmer Ray.
Run, run, run.

3
What's that?
It isn't a fox.

No! It's my kitty cat!

Run, Mandy May.
Run, run, run.

4
What's that?
It isn't a kitty cat!
Your cat's there!
In the sun.

5
Thank you!
Thank you, everyone!

2 **Circle all the animals in the story.**

Word Work

1 🐶 59 **Listen and chant.**

2 **Look and say. Then complete.**

1. r u n

2. ___ a b b i t

3. ___ u l e r

4. ___ e a d

3 Say and circle the words with the *u* sound.

1. (sun)

2. stop

3. mad

4. run

4  Say it!

> The rabbit runs in the sun.
> Run, rabbit, run!

UNIT 4 Picture Talk

1 Look at the picture. Match, then color.

1. doll

2. ball

3. kite

4. yo-yo

5. truck

6. teddy bear

Happy Reader

1 **Read and listen.**

In the Park

1
Brian and Nancy are in the park today.
The park is fun. Hooray!

See Brian's kite?
It's red, green, yellow, blue, and white.

2
Nancy: Hey! Look! Is it a ball?

Brian: No, it isn't. And it isn't a doll.

3

Nancy: What color is it? Is it blue?

Brian: No, it isn't. It's gray, and white, too.

Nancy: Is it an umbrella?

Brian: On a sunny day?
No, it isn't.
No way!

4

Nancy: It isn't an umbrella. It isn't a ball.

5

Brian: Look! It's an elephant. And it isn't small!

2 **Complete.**

It _____ an umbrella.

Happy Writer **Page 53**

Word Work

1 🐶 62 Listen and chant.

2 Look and say. Then complete.

1. <u>f</u> u n

2. ___ i v e

3. ___ o x

4. ___ o u r

3 Say, write, and match.

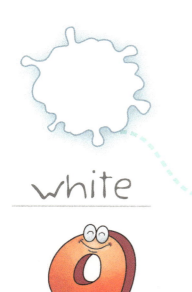
white

4  Say it!

The fun fox has five white kites.

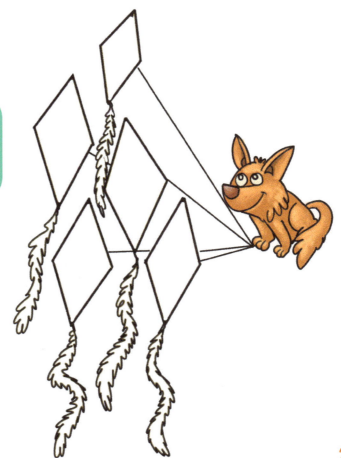

UNIT 5 Picture Talk

1 Look at the picture. Find and match.

1. ball  wall

2. crayon  floor

3. yo-yo  table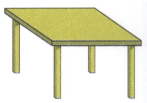

4. horse  window

5. cat  door

Happy Reader

1 64 Read and listen.

Oliver's Room

1
Oliver's room is a mess!
Where is the backpack?
It's on the floor!
And the kite is on the door.

Where is the pen? It's under the table.
And the towel is on the desk.
The map is on the bed.
Oh, what a mess!

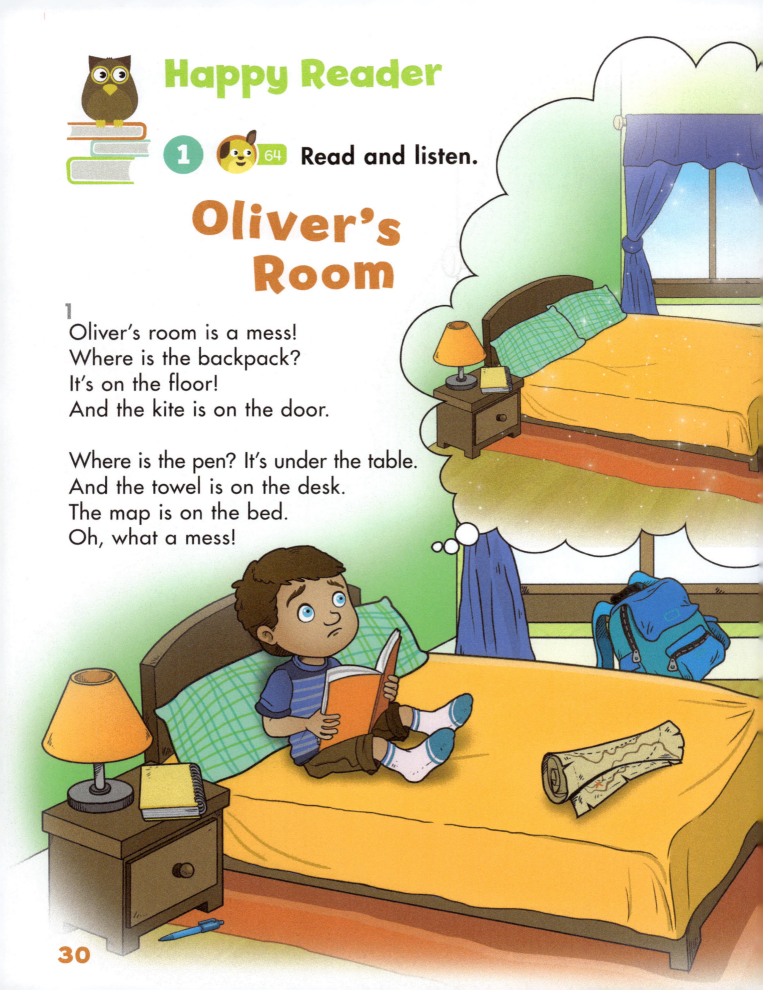

2

"Oliver, put the backpack on the chair.
Put the towel away.
Put the map in the backpack.
Then go out and play."

3

Dream of that!
Everything's back!
Now it's time for
a snack!

2 **Circle how mom is feeling.**

Mom is mad / happy.

Word Work

1 🐶 65 **Listen and chant.**

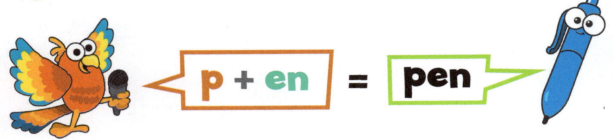

2 Say and circle the words with the *p* sound.

1. (pencil)

2. rabbit

3. picture

4. pen

3 Say, write, and match.

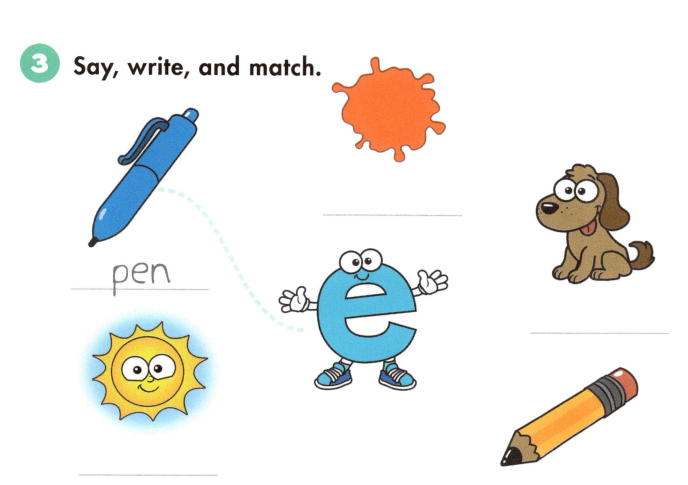

4   Say it!

Put the pencil and pen on the desk, please!

UNIT 6 — Picture Talk

1 Look at the picture. Find and color.

1. plants

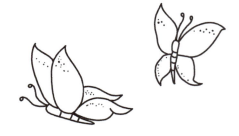

2. butterflies

3. frogs

4. trees

5. ladybugs

6. caterpillars

② Point, ask, and answer.

Happy Reader

1 🎧 67 **Read and listen.**

Nature Colors

1

What are they?

They're orange butterflies and green frogs.

They're red ladybugs on brown logs.

2

Are they plants?
Are they bees?
They aren't rabbits.
What do you see?

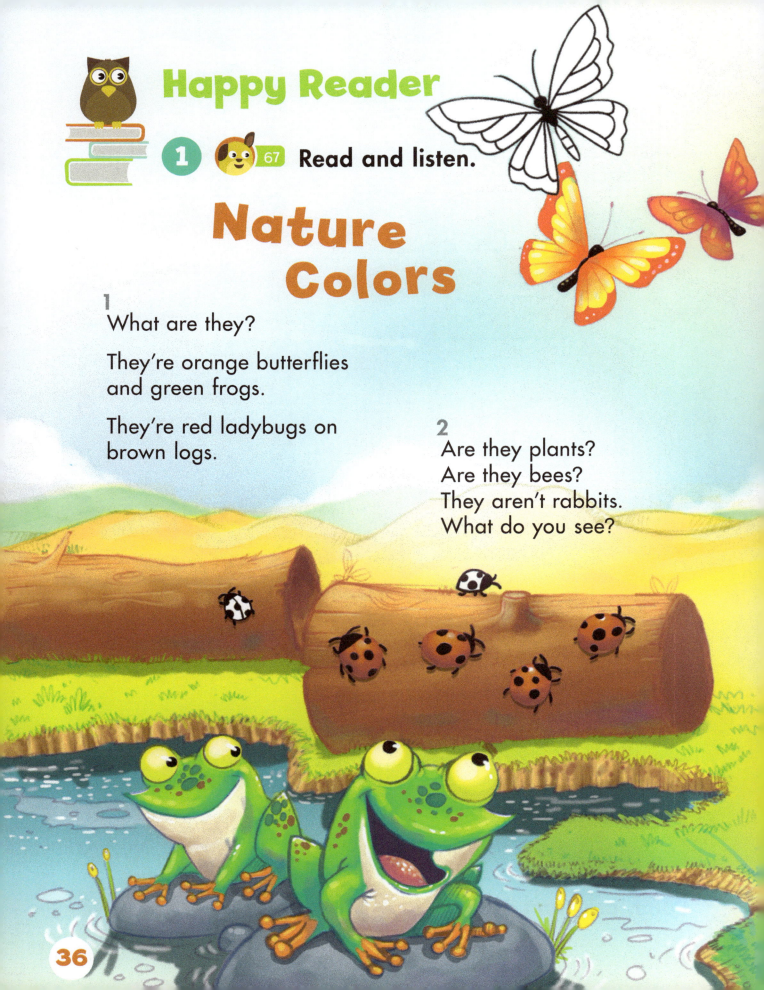

3 They're black ants on pink plants.
And yellow bees in big green trees.

4 They're caterpillars, gray and blue, beige and purple, and orange, too!

2 Color.

Happy Writer **Page 54**

Word Work

1 🐶 68 **Listen and chant.**

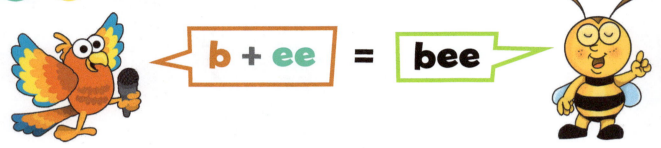

b + ee = bee

2 **Look and say. Then complete.**

1. butterflies

2. ___ e e s

3. ___ i g

4. ___ e i g e

3   Say, write, and match.

tree

4    Say it!

I see butterflies and bees in big green trees.

UNIT 7  Picture Talk

1 Look at the picture. Find and match.

1.    bedroom

2.    dining room

3.    bathroom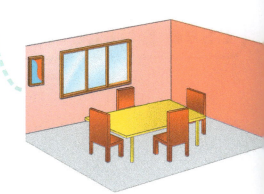

4.    kitchen

2 Point and say.

Happy Reader

1   **Read and listen.**

Hide-and-Seek

1
Let's play hide-and-seek!
One, two, three, four, five!
Six, seven, eight, nine, ten!
Eleven, twelve, thirteen,
fourteen, fifteen!
Sixteen, seventeen, eighteen,
nineteen, twenty!
Here I come!

2
How many people
are there?

There's Jenny!
Wave hello, Jenny!
I see you!

3
There are twelve crayons in the bedroom.
There is one window, too.
How many people are there?

There's Kristy.
Wave hello, Kristy! I see you!

4
Now, where is Buster?
Is he in the living room?
Is he under the chair?

Look! There he is!
Buster's right there!

2 **Number the friends in order.**

☐ Buster ☐ Jenny ☐ Kristy

Happy Writer **Page 55**

Word Work

1  **Listen and chant.**

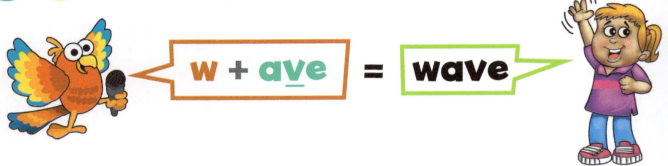

2 Look and say. Then complete.

1. ___ i n d o w

2. ___ a l l

3. ___ a v e

3 Say, write, and match.

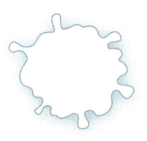  

name

4 72 Say it!

Wave hello to the snake in the window!

UNIT 8 — Picture Talk

1 Look at the picture. Find and check (✓) or cross (✗).

1. [✓] hamburger

2. [ ] hot dog

3. [ ] cookie

4. [ ] milk

5. [ ] French fries

6. [ ] pizza

2 **Point and say.**

Happy Reader

1 🐶 73 **Read and listen.**

Freddy the Food Monster

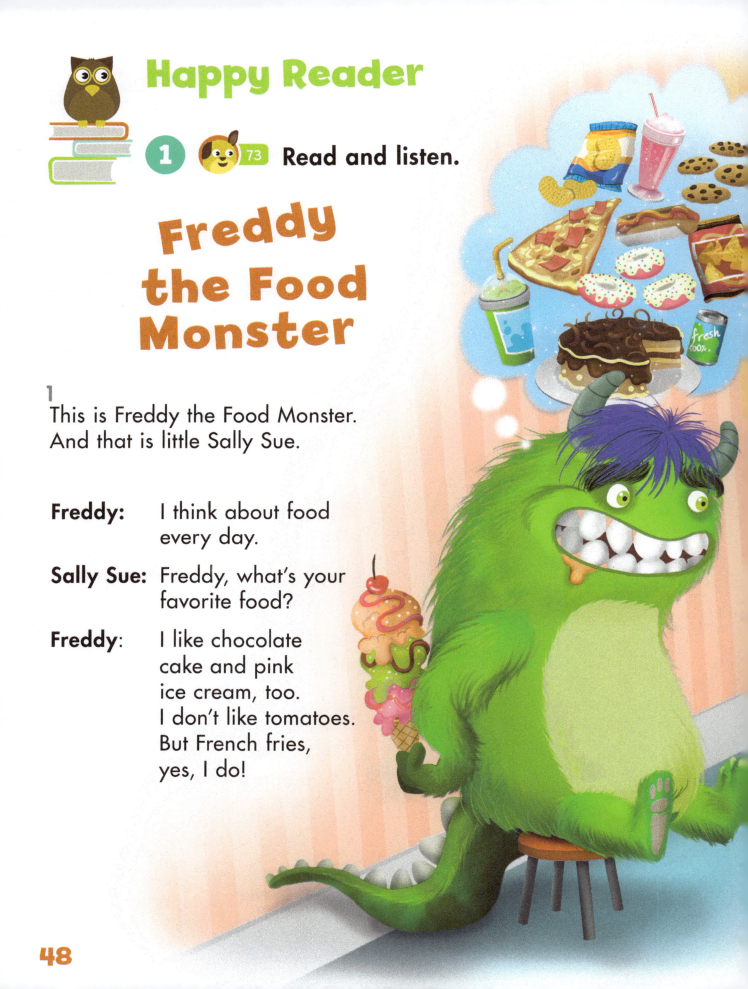

1

This is Freddy the Food Monster. And that is little Sally Sue.

Freddy: I think about food every day.

Sally Sue: Freddy, what's your favorite food?

Freddy: I like chocolate cake and pink ice cream, too. I don't like tomatoes. But French fries, yes, I do!

2

Sally Sue: Oh, Freddy! Tomatoes are good for you!

Freddy: I like cookies and milk. I don't like carrots and peas.

Sally Sue: Freddy! Cake, ice cream, and cookies are bad for you. Eat apples, oranges, and bananas, please! Fruit is good for you!

2 **Check (✓) Freddy's favorite foods.**

1. ☐ cake
2. ☐ apples
3. ☐ cookies
4. ☐ French fries

Happy Writer **Page 55**

Word Work

1  Listen and chant.

th + ink = think

2 Say, write, and match.

think

3 Look and say. Then complete.

1. k _i_ t c h e n

2. p __ n k

3. m __ l k

4. s __ x

4  Say it!

> The three sisters like pink milk in the kitchen.

Happy Writer

Unit 1 Family Fun Page 6

1 Complete.

1. d a d

Jo

2. m _ _

3. b _ o _ h _ r

4. _ i _ e _

Unit 2 Hopscotch Winner Page 12

1 Complete and write numbers.

Box number o n e!
Now _ w _, three,
f _ _ r, five, s _ _ _,
seven, ei _ _ t,
nine, _ _ _ !

Unit 3 Kitty Cat Page 18

1 Complete.

I t ___ s ___'t a kitty cat.

It's an o___ o___ u___.

Unit 4 In the Park Page 24

1 Complete.

1.

   Is it _____ _____ ?

2.

   It's _____ _____ .

Happy Writer

Unit 5 Oliver's Room Page 30

1 Complete.

1.

2.

The _____ is the _____.

The _____ is the _____.

Unit 6 Nature Colors Page 36

1 Complete, draw, and color.

They're r_e_d ladybugs on br__w__ logs.

Unit 7 Hide-and-Seek   Page 42

1 **Complete.**

1. Jenny is in the k_t_e_.

2. Kristy is in the _e_r__m.

3. Buster is in the _i_i_g_r__m.

Unit 8 Freddy the Food Monster   Page 48

1 **Complete and draw.**

I like _____ , _____ , and _____ .

Macmillan Education
4 Crinan Street
London N1 9XW
A division of Springer Nature Limited

Companies and representatives throughout the world

ISBN 978-0-230-47074-3

Text, design, and illustration © Springer Nature Limited 2015
Written by Angela Llanas and Libby Williams
The authors have asserted their rights to be identified as the authors of this work in accordance with the Copyright, Designs and Patents Act 1988.

Happy Campers is a trademark, property of HM Publishers Holdings Limited

First published 2015

All rights reserved; no part of this publication may be reproduced, stored in a retrieval system, transmitted in any form, or by any means, electronic, mechanical, photocopying, recording, or otherwise, without the prior written permission of the publishers.

Original design by Pronk Media Inc.
Page make-up by Victory Productions, Inc.
Illustrated by Victory Productions, Inc.
Cover design and illustration by Roberto Martínez
Cover photograph by George Contorakes

Commissioned photographs by George Contorakes, pp. 5, 11, 17, 23, 29, 35, 41, 47

The authors and publishers wish to thank the following for their help with the photo shoot:
Karen Greer Models, LLC; Chloe; Christian; Christopher; and Zoey

These materials may contain links for third party websites. We have no control over, and are not responsible for, the contents of such third party websites. Please use care when accessing them.

Printed and bound in Great Britain by Ashford Colour Press Ltd.
2019
11